FRÉDÉRIC CHOPIN
AN INTRODUCTORY ALBUM

THE ASSOCIATED BOARD OF
THE ROYAL SCHOOLS OF MUSIC

INTRODUCTION

It hardly seems appropriate to include an album of Chopin (1810-1849) in a series of 'Easier Piano Pieces', since none of his works can be considered easy to play, either technically or interpretatively; but no collection of music for the piano would be complete without some sort of introduction to one of the greatest composers for this instrument. The pieces in this selection – five Preludes, five Mazurkas, three Waltzes, one Nocturne and five miscellaneous items – have been chosen for their comparative lack of technical difficulty in the hope that a study of these works, even if they cannot be completely mastered, may lead to an appreciation of Chopin's lyrical genius.

One of the fundamental problems in preparing works of Chopin for publication is that of establishing authentic texts. Apart from the fact that Chopin was not always consistent in what he wrote, one has to take into account, in some cases, varying autographs and, in others, differing early editions. Further, not only did he make revisions to his manuscripts and printed editions, but he also discussed possible amendments with friends and pupils. In consequence, with the popularity of his work after his death, a multiplicity of editions (Mikuli, Klindworth, Schultz etc.) appeared, each vying with the others in presenting 'improved' texts. In this album it has not been thought necessary to consider all the different readings in detail, but some of the more significant points are mentioned in footnotes: in particular, in the Waltz in A flat, where our source is the edition published posthumously by Chopin's friend from childhood days, Julius Fontana, which differs in many respects from the autograph.

Editorial interpolations for which there is no authority are shown within square brackets for dynamics, tempi, pedalling, marks of articulation etc. and by a vertical stroke through a slur or phrase in marks of expression. A metronome mark, appearing at the beginning of a piece, has been taken from the original edition; whereas a metronome mark at the end of a piece is only an editorial suggestion and in no way authoritative.

All the trills in the pieces in this album should begin and end on the principal note. Small notes should be played on the beat and not before it.

ALAN JONES
London 1985

PRELUDE
in B minor

Op. 28 No. 6
composed 1831
published 1839

Lento assai

AB 1903

MAZURKA
in A minor

Op. post. 68　No. 2
composed 1827
published 1855

(a) A similar ending to the trill can be used throughout the piece.

AB 1903

PRELUDE
in A

Op. 28 No. 7
composed 1837
published 1839

(a) For a small hand the lower A♯ may be omitted.

LARGO

Op. post.
composed ? 1837
published 1938

AB 1903

As in the Prelude below, the second section of the Largo may be repeated, with changes to the dynamics.

[♩ = c. 63]

PRELUDE
in C minor

GRADE 5! Op. 28 No. 20
composed 1838
published 1839

(a) There is evidence that the flat, although not in the original notation, was intended by Chopin.

[♩ = c. 50]

AB 1903

WALTZ
in A minor

Op. post.
composed ? 1843
published 1955

Allegretto

$[\, \textbf{J} = \text{c.126}\,]$

MAZURKA
in A flat

Op. 24 No. 3
composed 1835
published 1836

Moderato con anima, ♩ = 126

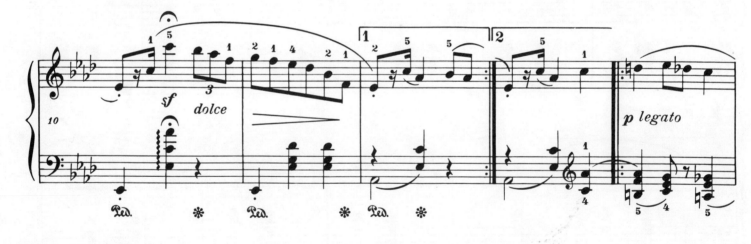

AB 1903

CANTABILE

Op. post.
composed 1834
published 1931

[Andante con moto]

[♪ = c. 96]

FUNERAL MARCH

Op. post. 72 No. 2
composed 1827
edited & published by Fontana 1855

Tempo di Marcia, ♩ = 84

TRIO

GRADE 6

MAZURKA
in G minor

Op. post. 67 No. 2
composed 1842
published 1855

(*a*) In some editions, sevenths (*D-C*) are preferred to octaves in bars 9 & 49.

(*b*) For a small hand, this chord may be broken.

AB 1903

PRELUDE
in E minor

Op. 28 No. 4
composed 1837
published 1839

GRADE 6.

AB 1903

[♩ = c. 56]

WALTZ
in A minor

Op. 34 No. 2
composed 1831
published 1838

1) In the original editions, the right-hand reading in bars 8, 160 & 196 is: [music example]. The evidence for this later reading comes from a pencilled revision by the composer.

AB 1903

MAZURKA
in C

Op. 33 No. 3
composed 1838
published 1838

GRADE 6

(a) In the original German edition, the F here is sharpened.

AB 1903

(b) Some editions introduce ties here by analogy with bar 20.

AB 1903

GRADE 7.

NOCTURNE
in G minor

Op. 15 No. 3
composed 1833
published 1833

* Chopin's own metronome mark seems somewhat fast.

(a) For a small hand, this chord may be broken.

ECOSSAISE
in G

Op. post. 72 No. 3/2
composed 1826
published 1855

[♩ = c. 96]

PRELUDE
in D flat

Op. 28 No. 15
composed 1838
published 1839

(a) In the autographs and the original editions, the left-hand minims in bars 2, 5, 6, 21, 24 & 25 are not dotted.

AB 1903

(b) In the autographs and original editions, this chord appears as an octave C♯, but Chopin later revised it.

[♩ = c. 72]

MAZURKA
in G sharp minor

Op. 33 No. 1
composed 1837
published 1838

* The tempo of this Mazurka is uncertain. *Mesto* appears in the autograph and the original German edition, whereas *Presto* appears in the original French edition. According to another source, Chopin later changed *Presto* for *Lento*.

(a) In the autograph and the original German edition, the G's in bars 2 & 38 are not tied.

[♩ = c. 116]

ALBUM LEAF

Op. post.
composed 1843
published 1910

[♩ = c. 92]

AB 1903

WALTZ "L'adieu"
in A flat

Op. post. 69 No. 1
composed 1835
edited & published by Fontana 1855

Chopin's autograph differs from the first published edition by Fontana in a number of places—most notably: *(a)* the third beat is a dotted quaver and semiquaver; *(b)* the first beat is a crotchet Eb followed by a turn before the acciaccatura; *(c)* a semiquaver rest and eight semiquaver notes constitute the first two beats; *(d)* 𝅘𝅥𝅮 .

AB 1903

(e) staccato quaver as in b.42;   (f)

AB 1903

(h) the final section is a repeat of bb. 1-16 (without the variation in b.123).

AB 1903

Reproduced and printed by Halstan & Co. Ltd., Amersham, Bucks., England